The Oregon Trail

by
Francis Parkman

adapted by
Norman Weiser

Illustrations by
Dave Simons

MOBY BOOKS

PLAYMORE, INC., Publishers
Under arrangement with I. WALDMAN & SON, INC.
New York, New York

ILLUSTRATED CLASSIC EDITIONS

edited by

Malvina G. Vogel

Copyright © 1979 by

I. WALDMAN & SON, INC.
New York, New York

MOBY BOOKS is a trademark of
I. Waldman & Son, Inc.
18 East 41st Street, New York, New York 10017

Contents

About the Author

As a boy in Boston, Francis Parkman preferred roaming the woods and reading about Indians to reading his school books. A classmate said he had "Injuns on the brain." His fascination with Indians, especially those who had not been changed by contact with the white man, would lead him on a 2,000-mile, six-month journey into the wilderness of the American West. The result was *The Oregon Trail* and a series of other books recounting the struggle between France and England for North America.

In 1846, the 23-year-old Parkman, fresh out of Harvard College, began what he called his "tour of curiosity and amusement to the Rocky Mountains."

His health, poor before he even began his journey, was further weakened by the hardships of travel. Therefore, after his return, he had to dictate the story of his travels to his cousin and friend, Quincy Shaw, who had accompanied him on the journey.

The Oregon Trail first appeared as a series of magazine articles in 1847, and as a book in 1849. It is now a classic of life in the early West before the Gold Rush of 1849.

Despite his weakening eyesight and crippling arthritis, which at times were so bad that he could write no more than six lines a day, Parkman went on to research and write the eight volumes of his great history of the English and French in the New World before he died in 1893.

People You Will Meet

Francis Parkman, *a young man who travels west to study Indian life*

Quincy Shaw, *Parkman's cousin who accompanies him on his journey*

Deslauriers, *a teamster who tends the horses and mules on the trip*

Henry Chatillon, *a brave hunter and guide*

Kearsley, *a wagon-train captain*

Captain C—
Jack } *three Englishmen who travel across America on a hunting expedition*
Mr. R—

Old Smoke
Red Water
The Whirlwind } *Sioux Indian chiefs*
Big Crow

Raymond, *a Canadian hunter*

Reynal
McCluskey } *traders*

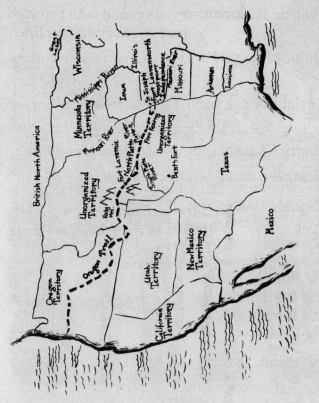

The Oregon Trail

Dressed for the Journey

CHAPTER 1

The Frontier

"Francis Parkman!" exclaimed my friend and cousin, Quincy Adams Shaw. "If our classmates at Harvard and our parents back in Boston could see us now!"

"Well, Quincy," I said, "if we wish to study the savage Indians closely, the only sure way to do it well is to meet them face to face on their home ground. So we must travel as far west as the Rocky Mountains to do it. And we must be properly dressed and equipped for so difficult a journey." I looked at his outfit, then at mine, and added, "And so we are."

We wore red flannel shirts belted around the waist, buckskin leggings, and moccasins. Heavy pistols hung in our holsters on plain black Spanish saddles. Quincy carried a double-barreled shotgun, while I had a 15-pound rifle. Beneath the protective white covering of our small cart lay our provisions — a tent, ammunition, blankets, food, and presents for the Indians.

"An outfit," I said, glancing from Quincy's clothing to horses to mules to cart, "more suitable for hard use than for decoration."

It was May of 1846. Quincy and I were in Westport, on the Missouri River. Westport was considered the dividing line, or the "jumping-off" place from the United States' western frontier to the wilderness. Beyond that wilderness lay Oregon and California, each with about four thousand American settlers. But in 1846, nearly three thousand emigrants were making the dangerous journey

Loading the Cart with Provisions

west along the Oregon Trail.

Just one month ago, in April, we had arrived in St. Louis. The city buzzed. Settlers from every part of the country were preparing for the journey to those distant western lands of promise. An unusual number of traders were making ready their wagons and outfits to head for Santa Fe, the capital of the Mexican province of New Mexico.

The hotels in St. Louis were crowded, and gunsmiths and saddlers were kept busy providing arms and equipment for the travelers. Steamboats were heading up the Missouri, crowded with passengers on their way to the frontier.

On April 28, Quincy and I left St. Louis in one of these steamboats. It was so heavily loaded with trade goods, wagons, mules, horses, saddles, harnesses, camp equipment, and travelers to Santa Fe and Oregon that it sat low in the water. It sat so low that the river

A Steamboat on the Missouri

splashed easily onto the deck.

For about a week the vessel struggled upward against the rapid current, sometimes running aground on sand bars for several hours, sometimes grating on underwater tree branches. These branches were the limbs of trees that had grown along the shore before the wayward river had begun cutting into the bank, sending them crashing down into the muddy stream. Some then became lodged in the river bottom, ready to punch holes in any unhappy steamboat that should pass over them.

As we traveled along the river, we began to see signs of the grest western movement that was then taking place. Parties of settlers, with their tents and wagons, were camping on open spots near the river on their way to the common meeting-place at Independence, Missouri.

When the boat pulled into Independence

Branches Lodged in the River Bottom

landing, I saw on shore broad-hatted Mexicans who worked for the Santa Fe traders, long-haired, buckskin-clad French hunters just returned from the mountains, and many tall, strong men with rifles — the latest of that fearless band of pioneers whose axes and rifles were opening a path from the Allegheny Mountains to the western prairies. Now they were probably bound for Oregon, which was a more challenging and exciting territory for their restless spirits than any territory on this side of the great plains.

The town was crowded. New parties of settlers were constantly passing through to join the thousand or more emigrants camped out on the prairie about eight miles away. The streets were thronged with men, horses, and mules. There was an unending hammering and banging from a dozen blacksmith shops where wagons were being repaired, and horses and oxen shod.

At Independence Landing

A train of emigrant wagons from Illinois had stopped in the main street. Healthy children's faces peeped out from under the wagon covers. Here and there, a plump maiden sat on horseback, holding a faded parasol over her sunburned face. The men, sober-looking farmers, stood about their oxen with whips in their hands. I looked at them all and thought, "Why are they going west? Is it a mad hope for a better life, a desire to shake off the binding rules of law and society, or mere restlessness? Will they be sorry they made the journey?"

When we reached the Kansas landing about 500 miles from the mouth of the Missouri, we left the boat and stored our equipment at a tavern while we set out in a wagon for Westport. There, we hoped to buy horses and mules for our journey.

Westport was full of Indians: Sacs and Foxes with shaved heads and painted faces,

An Emigrant Wagon

Shawnees and Delawares in calico frocks and turbans, Wyandots dressed like white men, and a few wretched Kansas Indians wrapped in old blankets. They strolled about the streets, while their little shaggy ponies were tied by the dozens along fences and rails.

As we stood at the door of a tavern, a familiar face appeared. I would have recognized that ruddy face and bristly red beard and moustache anywhere. It was Captain C— of the British Army who, with his brother Jack and Mr. R—, an English gentleman, were setting out on a hunting expedition across the continent. We had met them earlier in St. Louis, and here they were again.

After the usual exchange of greetings, Captain C— got serious.

"Mr. Parkman," he said, "our number's too small for a journey alone into the mountains. It struck us that since you and Mr. Shaw here were bound that way too, as you told us in St.

Meeting Captain C— of the British Army

Louis, you might wish to join us. Reinforcements, as it were."

"Surely, Captain C—," I replied, "you must have thought of going with one of those emigrant parties?"

Very distastefully, he said, "Oh no, Mr. Parkman! Not with those Kentucky fellows! You and Mr. Shaw are *gentlemen*. Anyone can see that. Now what do you say? Remember, if we travel together, in union there is strength."

I turned to Quincy and asked, "Well, what do you think?"

"Sounds like a good arrangement to me," he said.

"Splendid!" the captain almost shouted. "Then it's settled."

We agreed on the route we would take traveling west. Then, since we still had to complete our preparations, we promised to meet our new friends at the Kansas crossing, where they would wait for us.

"Not with Those Kentucky Fellows!"

We purchased horses and mules and hired a cheerful Canadian, Deslauriers, to manage our animal team. The fourth human member of our own little group was a Frenchman we had hired in St. Louis to be our guide. This was Henry Chatillon, a six-foot-tall, powerful yet graceful hunter who had spent half his thirty years in the mountains. It was said that he had killed more than one grizzly bear for every year of his age. I would later discover that nowhere in the city or in the wilderness would I ever meet a better or braver man than my true-hearted friend, Henry Chatillon.

One day as we were nearing the completion of our travel preparations, we were introduced to the prairie thunderstorm. The sharp, unceasing lightning flashes and the stunning, continuous thunder were phenomena I had never known before. But I would become quite familiar with them before this journey ended. Slanting sheets of rain fell with a heavy roar

Henry Chatillon

and rose in a spray from the ground, so as to completely hide the woods. The streams swelled so rapidly, we could hardly cross them. About sunset, the storm cleared away. Then the sun streamed from the breaking clouds upon the swift, angry Missouri and on the vast expanse of forest that stretched from its banks back to the distant bluffs.

Our preparations were almost concluded when we received a message from Captain C—.

"Listen to this, Quincy," I said. "They're going to meet us at Fort Leavenworth instead of at the Kansas crossing. It seems they've decided we'll take an army trail from there to the emigrant road."

"But, Francis, that's not the route we agreed on," argued Quincy, as annoyed as I was. "They've changed it without consulting us."

"Yes, Quincy," I said. "It *is* high-handed of them. But there's nothing we can do about it

The Prairie Thunderstorm

now. Fort Leavenworth it will be."

And so, one fine morning in May, our little parade of four men, eight animals, and one cart set out. Henry Chatillon, on his gray Indian pony, was in the lead. He wore a white blanket coat, broad felt hat, fringed buckskin leggings, and moccasins. His knife was stuck in his belt, and his bullet pouch and powder horn hung at his side. His rifle lay before him, resting against the high pommel at the front of his saddle. Quincy and I rode behind him, and bringing up the rear was Deslauriers, with the mules and cart, wading ankle-deep in the mud. One moment he was puffing at his pipe and the next, hurling French curses at the stubborn mules.

It was not a promising start. First, the mule attached to the cart refused to pull. He reared and plunged, burst ropes and straps, and nearly flung the cart into the Missouri.

Then, when Westport was scarcely out of

The Little Parade Sets Out.

sight, as we were trying to cross a deep muddy gully—another feature of prairie experience that afterward became too familiar to us—the cart stuck fast. It took an hour to free it.

On dry land again, we looked around. Behind us was the great forest that once spread from the western plains to the shores of the Atlantic. Before us lay the green, ocean-like expanse of prairie, stretching clear to the horizon.

That night, in a meadow on the banks of the Kansas River, we put up our tent for the first time. Since there were no trees in the meadow, we hobbled the horses, or tied their forelegs together, in the grass to prevent their running off. With Deslauriers in a cubbyhole in the cart and the three of us lying in the tent upon blankets spread on the ground, using our saddles for pillows, our little party spent its first night in the open, serenaded by the voices of whippoorwills.

The First Night's Camp

Parkman Is Angry with Mr. R—.

CHAPTER 2

"Jumping Off"

Another day and a half brought us to Fort Leavenworth and to the nearby camp of our British fellow-travelers. After supper, we held a council by the ruddy light from a distant prairie grass fire.

We learned that Mr. R—, the Englishman, had taken command of his group in Westport, and what he had to tell us caused quite a bit of anger among us.

"Do you mean to say," I asked him in complete amazement, "that although you took it on yourself to change the route we'd all agreed on—and to do so without consulting us—not a single one of you knows the way?"

"Now, now, Parkman," broke in R—, soothingly. "No need to be concerned. We'll just follow the trail from here of those cavalry companies who rode up to Fort Laramie last summer. Their route will take us to the Platte River, and from there we shall follow the trail of the Oregon emigrants up the valley of the Platte. Easiest thing in the world. Now I suggest we 'jump off' day after tomorrow."

But Quincy and I did not share R—'s confidence. The next day, we rode a few miles beyond Fort Leavenworth to visit with the trader at a Kickapoo Indian village. There, we shared good wine and said our farewells.

By sunrise of the following morning, all was prepared, and we "jumped off." Riding in advance, I looked back and saw the line of scattered horsemen stretching for a mile or more. Far in the rear crept the white wagon of

"Jumping Off"

our English companions. It was drawn by six mules and crammed with provisions for six months and enough ammunition for an army.

Quincy and I still felt uneasy at R—'s route.

After a ride of an hour or two, a familiar cluster of buildings appeared ahead. "Hallo!" shouted a voice. "Where are you going?"

It was the Kickapoo trader. We had gone miles out of our way and had not advanced an inch toward the Rocky Mountains. So we turned in the direction he indicated, Quincy and I exchanging knowing looks.

With the sun for a guide, we headed across the plain. We struggled through thickets. We waded brooks. We crossed green prairies expanding before us mile after mile.

"Here's the way at last!" shouted the captain as he spotted the tracks of a large body of horsemen. With our tempers somewhat improved, we turned joyfully and followed this new course.

"Here's the Way At Last!"

The next morning, our trail led us to a stream that was wide and deep, and looked particularly muddy. Deslauriers, now in the lead with his cart, jerked the pipe from his mouth and urged his mules on with his whip and some choice French curses. In plunged the cart. It got halfway across the stream, then stuck fast. Deslauriers leaped into the stream knee-deep and, with whip and curses flying even harder and faster, coaxed the mules out of the mud.

Our English friends' long team and heavy wagon approached, but Wright, their teamster, stopped on the brink.

"Now my advice is . . . ." began the captain.

"Drive on!" cried R—.

But Wright hadn't made up his mind yet what to do, so he sat quietly on one of the mules, whistling to himself.

"My advice is," continued the captain, "that we unload the cart. Otherwise, we shall surely

Deslauriers' Whip and Curses Fly.

stick in the mud."

"Drive on! Drive on!" cried R— impatiently.

Meanwhile, Wright had made up his mind. He suddenly whipped his six mules and loosed a stream of rich American curses and oaths that, after Deslauriers' French, sounded like the roaring of a heavy cannon after the pops of firecrackers. The mules dived into the mud. Wright lashed and swore like a madman until the animals reached the far bank. As for the wagon, it was hub-deep in the mud and settling deeper every moment. There was nothing to do now but unload the wagon, dig out the wheels, and build a path of bushes and branches to dry land.

Interruptions like this occurred four or five times a day for two weeks, slowing considerably our progress to the Platte River.

The grassy plains were a beautiful scene. But the traveler, however enthused at the scenery, will find his wagons sticking in the

Rescuing the Englishmen's Wagon

mud, his horses breaking loose, his harness giving way, and his wagon axles proving unsound. But he will find his bed to be a soft one — of the richest black mud!

For food, the traveler must content himself with biscuits and dried salted meats, for — strange as it may seem — this region produces little game. Indeed, as he advances, he will see, crumbling in the grass, the vast antlers of the elk and, farther on, the whitened skulls of the buffalo that once swarmed over this now deserted land.

Yet, to make up for this unexpected lack of game, the traveler will find himself beset with countless "varmints." Wolves will entertain him with a concert at night and skulk around him by day, just beyond rifle-shot. His horse will step into badger holes. From every marsh and mud-puddle will arise the bellowing, croaking, and trilling of legions of frogs. Numerous snakes will glide away from under

Seeing the Whitened Skull of a Buffalo

his horse's feet or quietly visit him in his tent at night, while the stubborn humming of clouds of mosquitoes will banish sleep from his eyelids.

When the traveler, thirsty with a long ride in the scorching sun, comes at last to a pool of water and attempts to drink, he will discover a troop of young tadpoles frolicking in the bottom of his cup.

Add to this prairie scene a sun that beats upon the traveler all morning with a suffocating, penetrating heat and a thunderstorm that rises and drenches him to the skin every afternoon at about four o'clock.

Such is travel upon the prairies!

One day, we happened upon four soldiers from Fort Leavenworth. After talking with them, Quincy reddened — but not from the prairie sun.

"That R—! Blast him!" he fumed, scowling. "Thanks to him we're lost again!"

Tadpoles Frolic in Parkman's Cup.

"What do you mean?" I asked. "What did those fellows say?"

"We've missed the trail entirely! Instead of moving toward the Platte, we've been heading for a village of Iowa Indians, nowhere near the Platte! That R—!"

Quincy went on more calmly. "Those soldiers said our best plan now is to head north until we reach the St. Joseph's trail. Some Oregon emigrants took that trail from St. Joseph, Missouri, a few weeks ago. That'll lead us west to the main Oregon trail."

We rode on in an extremely bad temper. After all our hardships, we still had not found the trail to Oregon — and now it would take longer than expected.

The next day, we arrived at the St. Joseph's trail and found the many tracks of the emigrants. We turned our horses' heads west, towards Fort Laramie. It would be a 700-mile trip — *if* we did not get lost again.

"We've Missed the Trail Entirely!"

The Sun Burns Down All Day.

CHAPTER 3

To the Platte

The journey was montonous. We would ride for hours over the unbroken carpet of fresh green grass without seeing a tree or a bush. Here and there a crow, a raven, or a turkey buzzard would interrupt the monotony.

But nothing interrupted the monotony of the weather. The sun burned down through a hazy sky all day. Towards evening, black thunderhead clouds rose fast above the horizon. Then deep mutterings of distant thunder began to roll hoarsely over the prairie, and soon the entire landscape turned purple in the inky shadows. Suddenly, a flash leaped out of the darkest fold of the cloud-filled sky and quivered down to the edge of the prairie. Thunder came in a sharp burst and a long rolling peal.

We managed to get the horses' legs hobbled together and the tents up just as the storm broke. The roaring torrents of rain completely shrouded the nearby trees and beat through the tent canvas in a fine drizzle, drenching us as thoroughly as if there had been no tent over us at all. The water dripped from the front of our caps and trickled down our cheeks. Several puddles collected around the tent pole, threatening to cover the entire tent floor.

Directly over our heads, the thunder burst with a terrific crash. It was not like the tame thunder of the Atlantic coast. No, this prairie thunder seemed to re-echo around the circle of the heavens with a strange and awful boom. The lightning flashed all night, revealing the

The Rain Beats Through the Tent.

vastness of the plain for a moment and then leaving us shut in as if by a solid wall of darkness.

We had spread rubber sheets between our blankets and the ground. The sheets kept the water out for a while, but when the growing puddles on the tent floor began to rise over their edges, the sheets served to keep the water *in* as well. By morning, we were sleeping in pools of rain water.

When we at last broke camp and set out, it was through mud and slime six inches deep.

In a few days, we came to the crossing of the Blue River. When Henry Chatillon saw that the river had become swollen by the rains and was now wider, deeper, and more rapid, he built a log raft. We unloaded the wagons, piled our goods on the raft and, with one of our men swimming at each corner, we towed the raft across. Then the empty wagons were easily passed over. We followed on horseback.

Building a Log Raft

By the time we camped near the spot where the St. Joseph's trail meets the main Oregon trail, we had been eight days without meeting a single human being. But we had found many sad traces of the emigrants' progress. Sometimes we would pass the grave of one who had sickened, died, and was buried on the journey. The earth on the grave was usually torn up and covered with wolf tracks. Other times we would come upon a piece of plank standing on the summit of a grassy hill, and on it would be something like the following, inscribed, probably, with a red-hot piece of iron, "Mary Ellis. Died May 7th, 1845. Aged two months."

Imagine then the surprising effect on us, as we lay around our evening campfire amid the loneliness of the prairie, of hearing the distant and faint voices of men and women.

The next morning we overtook the emigrant caravan whose tracks we had been following.

By the time we camped near the spot where the St. Joseph's trail meets the main Oregon trail we had seen scores which... looking

MARY ELLIS
DIED MAY 7th
1845
AGED
TWO MONTHS

An Emigrant's Grave

Its twenty heavy, white-covered wagons were creeping on in slow procession, with a large herd of cattle following behind.

As we pushed rapidly by the wagons, children's faces poked out from behind the white coverings to look at us, and care-worn, thin-faced mothers seated in front stopped their knitting to stare at us in curiosity.

By the side of each wagon walked the husband, urging on his oxen, inch by inch. Some of the men looked enviously at us as we rode lightly and swiftly by.

We soon left them far behind. But our English companions' wagon became stuck in a deep, muddy ditch, and by the time we got it out, the wagon train had passed us.

But the emigrants soon stopped to camp, and again we rolled on past them. When we stopped to rest and dine, I noticed that R— was missing and mentioned it to Quincy.

"The captain told me that R— stayed

The Emigrant Wagons Pass.

behind with the emigrants to have one of their blacksmiths shoe his horse," Quincy explained.

I was suspicious. "Well, Quincy, he should have been back by now . . . unless something's afoot. I don't like it one bit."

"Yes, Francis, I . . . look!" Quincy pointed to a hilltop a mile off, where R— and his horse appeared against the sky, followed by a huge white object.

"What is that blockhead bringing with him now?" I muttered. A moment later, my question was answered as, slowly and solemnly, one behind the other, four ox-drawn wagons rolled over the crest of the hill and descended toward our camp.

It seemed that some of the emigrants wanted to go back, while others insisted on pushing forward. Still others wanted to wait where they were until those they had left behind on the other side of the Blue River to

R— Returns with Emigrant Visitors.

await the birth of a baby rejoined them. It was the group who wanted to push forward — four wagons with ten men, one woman, and one small child — that R— had invited to join our party. We could not refuse them our protection because of the danger of Indians in this lonely land. But I did tell Kearsley, their leader, what we expected of them.

"We won't be delayed any more on our journey," I said. "If your oxen can't keep up with our mules, then you'll be left behind."

"Mr. Parkman," replied Kearsley, "our oxen *will* keep up. And if they can't, why, I'll find out how to make 'em do it."

As it happened, the next day our English companions broke the axle of their wagon. Kearsley's emigrant train lumbered by, and it was a week before we overtook it again!

We were now in the country of the thieving, murdering, and scalping Pawnee Indians. Every spring the Pawnees crossed from their

Parkman Warns Kearsley To Keep Up.

permanent winter villages on the lower Platte to their war and hunting grounds to the south. Our animals and our heads would be tempting targets for these bandits of the plains. So we began to take turns standing guard each night — two men in each of three shifts.

We did not know it until we caught up with Kearsley's party, but they had had an encounter with some Pawnees during the week we were separated. As Kearsley told it, "Well, sir, we was short of fresh meat, and when we seen these little black specks movin' way off, we figgered they was buffalo. 'Course none of us'd ever *seen* a buffalo afore, but that didn't make no never mind. They *had* to be buffalo. So the ten of us grabs our rifles and sets off, some on horseback and some on foot.

"After half an hour, we go over the top of this grassy ridge and find ourselves face to face with a passel of mounted Pawnees — 30 of 'em. I don't know who was more surprised,

Kearsley's Party Had Met Some Pawnees.

them or us. I reckon they figgered that even though they outnumbered us three to one, it was their bows and arrows to our guns, and they feared their time had come. So you never did hear such loud and friendly Indian welcomes and see such well-meanin' handshakes. Truth to tell, we was as glad as they was to get out of it with our scalps still on."

The day we rejoined the emigrants was the day we beheld the long-expected valley of the Platte. Even though it was a welcome sight, it was hardly a beautiful one. For mile after lonely mile, a vast plain as level as a lake spread out before us. It was crossed here and there by the Platte in a dozen threadlike channels. An occasional clump of woods rose in the middle of the plain like a shadowy island. No living thing moved through this vast landscape, except the lizards that darted over the sand and among the grass and prickly pears — a kind of cactus — at our feet.

The Long-Expected Valley of the Platte!

Fort Laramie was still 400 miles away — a journey of three weeks. We would be passing up the middle of a long sandy plain reaching nearly to the Rocky Mountains. On either side of the plain were lines of sand hills, broken in the wildest and most fantastic forms. And beyond these sand hills lay a barren, trackless waste, extending for hundreds of miles to the Arkansas River in one direction and to the Missouri in the other. Before and behind us, the level plain was unbroken as far as the eye could see. Sometimes the hot, bare sand of the plain glared in the sun. Sometimes the plain was covered by long, coarse grass. Skulls and whitening bones of buffalo were scattered everywhere.

The morning after we reached the Platte, a long procession of wretched savages passed near our camp. They were on foot, each leading his horse by a rope of bull hide. Their dress consisted merely of a kind of loin cloth and an

Buffalo Skulls and Bones Everywhere!

old buffalo robe, tattered and grimy, hanging over their shoulders. They carried their bows and arrows in their hands, while their lean little horses were laden with dried buffalo meat — the harvest of their hunting.

These were the Pawnees whom Kearsley had encountered the day before we caught up with his party. These Pawnees were the first examples — and rather unimpressive ones they were — of the genuine prairie savages.

Although we later learned that these Pawnees had attacked an emigrant party before us, I had a friendly conference with their chief, who received my gift of half a pound of tobacco with great pleasure.

"Look at it this way, Francis," Quincy said after they had gone, "they may seem friendly now, but I'm mighty glad we're with Kearsley's wagon train. After all, with ten more men available, we won't have to stand guard so often."

A Wretched Procession of Pawnees

Last Year's Tracks

CHAPTER 4

Buffalo!

Four days on the Platte and still no buffalo!
Last year's signs of them were plentiful. The
ground was covered with tracks and dimpled
with the low spots where the bulls had
wallowed in the hot weather. Buffalo
"chips" — their dried droppings — littered
the plain everywhere and made an excellent
substitute fuel for wood, which was extremely
scarce. But the animals themselves were not
to be seen.

One afternoon, Henry Chatillon and I rode
off a mile or two from the party in search of an
antelope. The vast plain waved with tall, thick

71

grass that swayed to and fro in billows with the breeze, sweeping our horses' bellies.

Suddenly, Henry shouted and pointed in the direction of the broken line of scorched, desolate sand hills on our left. There, a mile and a half away, two black specks slowly crossed the bare glaring face of a hill.

"Buffalo! Let us go!" he cried, whipping the sides of his hardy Indian pony.

We entered a ravine that wound like a snake among the hills. It was so deep that it completely hid us. We rode up the bottom of it, glancing through the bushes at its edge, until Henry abruptly jerked his rein and slid out of the saddle.

"There. You see?" he said.

I followed his pointing finger to a hill a quarter-mile distant. There, a long procession of buffalo marched in Indian file with the greatest dignity. Then more appeared from a hollow not far off, clambering up the grassy

"Buffalo!"

slope of another hill. A shaggy head and a pair of short, broken horns emerged from a ravine nearby, and with a slow, stately step, one by one the enormous brutes came into view, making their way across the valley, entirely unaware of any enemy.

Henry began crawling through grass and prickly pears towards his unsuspecting victims. He carried my rifle as well as his own, while I sat holding his horse's reins and wondering what he was up to. He was soon out of sight — and still the buffalo kept coming into the valley. For a long time all was silent.

Suddenly, in rapid succession, came the sharp blasts of two rifles. The whole line of buffalo quickened their pace into a clumsy trot and gradually disappeared over the ridge of the hill. Henry rose to his feet and stood looking after them.

"You've missed them," I said.

"Yes," said Henry. "Let us go." He came

Unsuspecting Victims

down into the ravine, loaded the rifles, and mounted his horse.

We rode up the hill after the buffalo. The herd was out of sight when we reached the top, but lying on the grass not far off was one buffalo, quite dead, and another, dying.

"You see how I miss them!" cried Henry joyously. He had fired from a distance of more than 150 yards, and both bullets had passed through the lungs — the true mark in shooting buffalo.

The darkness increased, and a driving storm came on. We tied our horses to the horns of the buffalo to keep the horses still in the storm, and Henry began the bloody work of cutting up the buffalo. He slashed away with the skill of an expert, while I vainly tried to imitate him. We tied the meat to the rawhide strings dangling at the back of our saddles and, with our horses heavily burdened with the better parts of the buffalo, we set out on our return.

"You See How I Miss Them!"

It was strangely dark during the storm, even though sunset was an hour off. We rode in driving sleet and cold rain through a large colony of prairie dogs. The little mounds of fresh earth around their holes were as numerous as the hills in a cornfield, but not a yelp was to be heard or a nose seen — they had all retired to the depths of their burrows. We envied them their dry, comfortable homes.

An hour's hard riding showed us our tent dimly looming through the storm. One side was puffed out by the force of the wind. We flung our piles of meat on the ground outside the tent, and Quincy, sitting inside, gave us a big smile of satisfaction.

A few days later on the trail, I heard from one of the men the cry of "Buffalo! Buffalo!" But it was only one grim old bull, roaming the prairie by himself.

"There may be more behind the hills," I shouted. "Come on, Quincy, Henry!"

Riding in Driving Sleet

We rode for over six miles, but the only living things we saw were wolves, snakes, and prairie dogs. The ground grew bad for a chase — steep hills and deep hollows, cut by frequent ravines not easy to pass. At last we saw a band of bulls. They were scattered, with some grazing on a green slope and the rest crowded together in the wide hollow below.

We rode toward them at an easy pace, bending close to our horses' necks. Instantly the bulls took the alarm. Those on the hill moved down; those below gathered into a mass. And all began shouldering each other along at a clumsy gallop. We followed, spurring our horses to full speed.

As the herd rushed through an opening in the hills, crowding and trampling in terror, we were close at their heels, half-suffocated by the clouds of dust. But as we drew near, their alarm and speed increased. Our horses, new to the work, showed signs of the utmost fear.

Bulls Grazing on a Slope

They bounded violently aside as we approached the buffalo and refused to enter the herd.

The buffalo now broke into several small groups, scampering over the hills in different directions. We followed, and I soon lost sight of Quincy. Neither of us knew where the other had gone. Pontiac, my horse, ran like a frantic elephant uphill and downhill, his heavy hoofs striking the prairie like sledge hammers. One moment he seemed eager, straining to overtake the panic-stricken herd. The next moment he was terrified and retreated.

At length, I urged Pontiac close behind a bull. I could clearly see the buffalo's shaggy mane and the tattered traces of last winter's hair which covered his back in uneven shreds and patches. This hair flew off in the wind as he ran. But neither my whip nor my spurs would bring Pontiac alongside him. So, from my unfavorable position, I fired.

Parkman Urges Pontiac Toward the Bulls.

The poorly-aimed bullet failed to stop the bull, because a buffalo must be shot in certain places on his body, or he will surely escape, as this one did.

As the herd was just disappearing behind the crest of the next hill, their short tails standing up and their hoofs twinkling through a cloud of dust, I heard Quincy and Henry shouting to me. But the sight of the buffalo had filled Pontiac with such terror that I could not halt his headlong rush. He was almost uncontrollable. I followed the herd up and over the ridge, with old Pontiac galloping among them at full speed, scattering them right and left.

Then one bull fell a little behind the rest, and after much effort I got Pontiac within six or eight yards of his side. The bull's back was darkened with sweat. He panted heavily, and his tongue hung down limply from his jaws.

Gradually coming up abreast of him, I urged

The Bull Pants Heavily.

Pontiac nearer to his side. Then suddenly, the bull did what all buffalo always do in such a situation. He slowed his gallop and, turning toward us, lowered his huge, shaggy head for a charge.

With a snort, Pontiac leaped aside in terror, nearly throwing me to the ground. The bull continued his flight, and I fired after him, but missed.

It was time, I decided, to draw rein and rejoin my friends. It was high time. The breath blew hard from Pontiac's nostrils, and the sweat rolled in big drops down his sides. I, myself, felt as if I were drenched in warm water. I looked around for some landmark to show me where I was and which way I ought to go. I might as well have looked for landmarks in the midst of the ocean! How many miles I had run or in what direction, I had no idea.

I was lost!

The Buffalo Lowers His Head for a Charge.

Parkman Checks His Compass.

CHAPTER 5

Lost! . . . and Found

I thought that by heading north, I should certainly find the Platte. So, with the aid of the compass hanging around my neck, I set off in that direction. I rode for two hours . . . but found no river.

I did not know that, at that point, the Platte veers off a good deal from its easterly course, and I was riding ever farther into a wild, endless expanse.

I thought hard. "Maybe the buffalo might prove my best guides," I decided, and I soon found one of the paths they had made in going to the river to drink. The path lay at right angles to my route, and when I turned Pontiac onto it, he pricked up his ears at the scent, assuring me I was right.

In the meantime, my ride had not been a lonely one. The face of the country was dotted far and wide with countless hundreds of buffalo. Antelope were very numerous and, with their natural curiosity, some would approach to look at me, gazing intently with their round black eyes. Then suddenly, they would leap aside and stretch lightly away over the prairie as swiftly as racehorses.

Wolves sneaked through the hollows and sandy ravines. Several times, I passed through prairie dog "towns," where each citizen sat at the mouth of his burrow, holding his paws before him as if in prayer. These prairie dogs yelped away most heartily, whisking their little tails with every cry.

Long checkered snakes sunned themselves in the midst of the "town," and little gray

Antelope Approach Parkman Curiously.

owls, with large white rings around their eyes, were perched side by side with the prairie dogs.

The prairie teemed with life — but none of it in human shape.

As I continued along the buffalo path, the prairie seemed to change. Only a wolf or two glided by now and then, never looking to right or left. For the first time, I noticed insects wholly different from those found farther east. Brightly colored butterflies fluttered about Pontiac's head. Strangely formed beetles, glittering with a metallic gleam, crawled on plants I had never seen before. Crowds of lizards darted like lightning over the sand.

I rode for a long time on the buffalo path until I reached the ridge of a sand hill. From there, I saw the pale surface of the Platte glistening in the midst of its desert valley and the faint outline of the hills beyond. Not a tree nor a bush nor a living thing was visible on

A Prairie Dog "Town"

that sun-scorched landscape.

In half an hour, I came upon the trail I had been seeking. It ran near the river. Seeing no tracks to show me that the party had passed, I turned east to meet them. I had been slightly ill on leaving camp in the morning, and six or seven hours of rough riding had wearied me extremely. So I soon stopped, flung my saddle on the ground and, with my head resting on it and Pontiac's trail rope tied loosely to my arm, I lay down to wait for the party to arrive.

At length, the white wagon coverings rose from the edge of the plain. By a strange coincidence, almost at the same moment, two horsemen appeared, riding down from the hills. As they got closer, I recognized them as Quincy and Henry. They had been out searching for me, even though they knew how useless the attempt was in such a broken country. They were now returning to the party, having just about given up hope.

Parkman Waits For the Party To Arrive.

Emigrants Wade Across the Platte.

CHAPTER 6

On the Trail to Fort Laramie

On June 8, we reached the usual crossing-place on the south fork of the Platte. The channel of the river, almost on a level with the plain, was one great sand bed about a half-mile wide. The average depth of the river here was not more than a foot and a half.

On the other side was an emigrant camp, and a few horsemen waded across to visit us. Their faces were anxious and care-worn—and with good cause. As one of them told us, "Ever since we left the settlements, there's been nothin' but trouble. Some of our folks died along the way. Pawnees got one feller. One evenin' a week ago, we were camped by the Platte when 600 Sioux come down on us, whoopin' and hollerin', and made off with our best horses. These they left ain't nothin' but buzzard bait.

"And then, the night we got here a guard fell asleep, and the wolves drove off a hunderd and twenny-three of our best cattle. We been days huntin' 'em. Don't know what we'll do if we don't find 'em. Worst part of the trip's still ahead."

They would be forced to yoke cows and heifers to their wagons and also to lighten the load. They would also have to leave behind a great part of their goods. I had seen many abandoned pieces of handsome furniture along the Platte. Perhaps some of them had been brought from England originally and packed in the family wagon for the endless journey to Oregon. Now, too heavy to carry farther, this handsome furniture lay bleaching and

The Emigrants Abandoned Their Furniture.

cracking on the hot prairie.

For too long now, we had been annoyed with our English companions. They made decisions without consulting us. They frequently insisted on making camp when we had gone no more than fifteen miles, thus slowing our progress when we wanted to speed it.

I discussed this situation with Quincy, Henry, and Deslauriers, and we made a decision, which I announced to Captain C—.

"We have decided to push ahead on our own to Fort Laramie," I told him. "We hope to reach the fort in four or five days of hard traveling."

And so, before sunrise the morning after we crossed the South Platte, we left the captain and his party with Kearsley's wagon train and rode off.

Four days of traveling took us through country where the horses waded in sand over their hoofs, where the sun scorched like fire,

Parkman Tells Captain C— He's Going On.

and where the air swarmed with sandflies and mosquitoes.

On the morning of the fifth day, we were crossing a plain when something came into view.

"Buffalo?" I asked Henry.

Henry reined in his horse and peered across the prairie with his more practiced eye. "Indians!" he said. "Old Smoke's lodges on the move, I b'lieve. Come, let us go!" And he galloped forward, with me riding by his side.

Before long, a black speck became visible on the prairie two miles off. It grew larger and larger, taking the form of a man and horse. Soon we could make out an Indian racing toward us at full gallop. Rider and steed bounded up to us and, with a sudden jerk of the rein, the Indian brought the wild, panting horse to a full stop.

We shook hands, as custom required. The Indian was a young fellow of the Sioux nation.

An Indian Races Towards Them.

Like most of his people, he was nearly six feet tall, well built, and graceful. He wore no paint and his head was bare. His long hair was gathered in the back, and attached to it, as a decoration and charm, was a whistle made from the wing bone of the war eagle and a line of glittering brass plates. This was a heavy ornament, but very popular and stylish among the Sioux.

The Indian's chest and arms were naked. The buffalo robe, worn over them when at rest, had fallen about his waist and was tied there by a belt. On his feet were gay moccasins. He carried a quiver, or arrow-case, of dogskin at his back and a crude but powerful bow over his shoulder. His horse had no bridle, only a cord of hair lashed around his jaw. The saddle, eighteen inches high at front and back, was made of wood covered with rawhide.

We rode with him to the Indian camp at Horse Creek. There, Henry greeted a large,

Greeting the Young Sioux

strong, nearly naked man. This was the chief, Old Smoke. Just behind him, his youngest and favorite squaw sat astride a fine mule which was covered with whitened skins decorated with beads and little metal ornaments.

The squaw had a spot of vermilion, a bright red paint, on each of her cheeks. In her hand she proudly carried the chief's tall lance upright. His round white shield hung at the side of her mule, and his pipe was slung at her back. Her deerskin clothes, made beautifully white by a kind of clay found on the prairie, was ornamented with beads and with long fringes at all the seams.

Warriors, women, and children swarmed like bees over the camp. Hundreds of dogs of all sizes and colors ran restlessly about. The wide shallow creek was alive with boys, girls, and young squaws, splashing, screaming, and laughing in the water.

This was merely a temporary Indian camp

Old Smoke and His Favorite Squaw

during the heat of the day, so no lodges were pitched. But the squaws of each lazy warrior had made him a shelter from the sun by stretching a few buffalo robes upon poles, and here he sat in the shade. Before him stood the badges of his rank as a warrior — his white bullhide shield, his "medicine" bundle, his bow and quiver, and his lance and his pipe, raised aloft on a tripod of poles.

Except for the dogs, the most active and noisiest tenants of the camp were the old women. They were as ugly as witches, with hair streaming loose in the wind and nothing but the tattered fragment of an old buffalo robe to hide their withered limbs. No longer favorites of their husbands, these old squaws performed the heaviest labors of the camp. They harnessed the horses, pitched the lodges, prepared the buffalo robes, and brought in meat for the hunters.

With the cracked voices of these hags, the

The Squaws Make Shelters for the Warriors.

barking of dogs, the shouting and laughing of children and girls, and the lazy quiet of the warriors, the whole scene had an effect too lively and striking to be forgotten.

After lunch, several Indians rode ahead with us. One of them, who must have weighed over 300 pounds, was called The Hog, because of his unusual size and certain features of his character. He straddled a little white pony that was hardly able to bear up under his enormous weight. The Hog was not a chief — he never had enough ambition to become one. He was not a warrior or a hunter — he was too fat and lazy. But he was the richest man in the village — he owned over 30 horses, and the Sioux judged a man's wealth by the number of horses he owned. He had ten times more than he needed, yet still his appetite for horses could not be satisfied.

Trotting up to me, The Hog shook my hand and gave me to understand he was my true

The Hog Shakes Parkman's Hand.

friend. Then, with his eyes twinkling out from between the folds of flesh that almost hid them, he began a series of signs and gestures. I knew nothing then of Indian sign language, so I called to Henry, "What is he saying?"

Henry watched and then smiled. "M'sieu, he wishes to make a bargain. He will trade one of his daughters for your horse."

"Henry," I said, "tell him, 'No, thank you.'"

The Hog saw my reply and, still laughing with the same good humor, gathered his robe about his shoulders and rode away.

The next day, since we were only seven miles from Fort Laramie, we attempted to clean ourselves up. We had not shaved in six weeks, so we hung up small mirrors against the trees and did so. Then we bathed in the muddy waters of the Platte as best we could.

"There!" exclaimed Quincy. "We're ready to appear among Fort Laramie society."

Preparing For Fort Laramie Society

Fort Laramie, on the Oregon Trail

CHAPTER 7

A Sioux Feast

Fort Laramie was one of the posts established by the American Fur Company, which pretty much controlled the Indian trade in this region. The fort lay about 700 miles beyond the westernmost outposts of American troops.

Built of sun-dried bricks made from clay, the fort was rectangular, with blockhouses at two of the corners, in addition to the one above the entrance. The clay walls stood about fifteen feet high, and rising from them was a palisade of slender stakes.

The open space inside was enclosed by little cabins, built right up against the walls. These were workshops, storerooms, and living quarters for the men employed at the fort or for the equally numerous squaws they were allowed to keep in it. The roofs of all these buildings served as gunners' platforms.

Part of the open space was set aside as a corral, into which horses and mules were crowded for safekeeping at night or in the presence of suspicious Indians visiting the fort.

Tall Indians, wrapped in their white buffalo robes, strode across the area or rested at full length on the low roofs of the buildings that surrounded it. Many squaws, gaily dressed, sat grouped in front of the rooms they occupied, as their restless and noisy half-breed children rambled in every direction through the fort. Trappers, traders, and employees of the fort were busy at their work or their

Indians and Traders Inside the Fort

amusements.

The morning after we arrived, Old Smoke's people were seen crossing Laramie Creek on their approach to the fort. The swift waters of the creek were alive with dogs, horses, and Indians. Some of the horses carried the long poles used in pitching the lodges. One end of each pole was tied to a rough packsaddle, the other dragged along the ground. A basket was tied between these poles, and those Indians' goods not piled on the horses' backs were carried in these baskets. Some of these baskets contained litters of puppies, broods of small children, or wrinkled old men. A great many of these curious vehicles — *travois*, the Canadians called them—splashed together through the creek. Among them swam countless dogs, often burdened with small *travois* as well.

The warriors dashed forward on horseback through this throng. The women sat perched

Old Smoke's People Approach the Fort.

on the packsaddles, adding to the burden of the already overloaded horses. The confusion was enormous. Dogs yelled and howled in chorus. Puppies in the *travois* whined, and little black-eyed children sputtered and clung fast to their baskets as the water splashed against their faces.

Before long, they all reached the bank, and soon the crowd melted away. Each family, with its horses and goods, filed off to the plain behind the fort, where, in half an hour, we saw sixty or seventy of their cone-shaped lodges rise up. Their horses were feeding by the hundreds over the surrounding prairie, and their dogs were roaming everywhere. The fort was full of warriors, and the Indian children were whooping and yelling endlessly under its walls.

Scarcely had these newcomers arrived when we saw a heavy caravan of emigrant wagons steadily advancing from the hills. They

Indian Lodges Outside the Fort

reached the river, plunged right in, and passed through. After they slowly lumbered up the bank, they rolled a quarter of a mile past the fort and the Indian village. Then they stopped and wheeled their wagons into a circle. In a short time, Fort Laramie was taken by storm, as the emigrants busied themselves buying or trading for the supplies needed for their journey onward.

Most of our evenings at Fort Laramie were spent in the Indian village, for the Indians looked on Quincy as something of a doctor and welcomed us warmly. Their most common complaint was severe inflammation of the eyes, caused by exposure to the sun. This, Quincy treated rather successfully with remedies from our small medicine chest.

On one visit, we sat on buffalo robes in Old Smoke's shabby tepee. Even though Old Smoke was their chief, the Sioux had a democratic community, and the chief never

Quincy Treats an Eye Inflammation.

lived better than anyone else, nor was he treated better than anyone else. Therefore, Quincy treated all, from the chief's own pretty daughter to the ugliest hag in the village.

As we sat watching Quincy at work, Smoke's oldest squaw entered the lodge and set before us a large wooden bowl of boiled dog meat — a Sioux delicacy.

Quincy and I looked at each other and gulped. But we knew that a dog feast was the greatest compliment a Sioux could offer his guest and that to refuse it would be an insult. So we attacked the dog feast and ate heartily.

After we finished, Old Smoke prepared his great pipe. He lit it, and we passed it from one to another, each inhaling a few puffs and handing it on, until the bowl was empty.

This done, we left our Indian friends and returned to the fort.

A Dog Feast with Old Smoke

The Whirlwind Calls For War.

CHAPTER 8

War!—War?

War!

During the preceding year, ten warriors of the Oglala band of the western Sioux nation, including the son of a chief called The Whirlwind, had been killed by the Snake, or Shoshone, Indians. Now, The Whirlwind was preparing for revenge. He called for a union of all the Sioux within 300 miles to punish the Shoshones, and upwards of 6,000 Indians were slowly creeping towards the meeting place, "La Bonté's Camp," on the Platte. There, some would begin their warlike ceremonies, then set out for the enemy country.

"Here's my chance, Quincy!" I said. "I came out here to study Indian life. Now, if you're with me, we can live in the midst of them . . . join a village . . . sleep in one of their tepees . . . see how they prepare for war! Let us be off to La Bonté's Camp!"

It did not happen just that way.

One morning, a young Indian brought unhappy news to us at the fort. The Horse, as this Indian was called, came to inform us that Henry's squaw lay dangerously ill in The Whirlwind's village, a few days' journey away.

Henry was anxious to see his squaw before she died and to provide for their children, whom he loved.

"We shall forget our plans to travel with Smoke's village to the rendezvous," I said. "Instead, we shall go with you to The Whirlwind's people."

"But, M'sieu," cried Henry, "you have been

The Horse Brings Bad News for Henry.

ill for several weeks, and you are unable to walk without pain and effort. I cannot permit you to go with me."

But I had made up my mind, and so had the rest of our party. On the twentieth of June we set out down the valley of Laramie Creek for The Whirlwind's village. Besides Deslauriers, Henry, Quincy, and myself, our traveling party included a long-haired Canadian named Raymond, whom we had hired for re-inforcement, and a trader named Reynal, who was traveling to the village as well. With Reynal was his squaw, Margot, whose 200 pounds sprawled in a *travois* basket, and her two nephews, The Horse, who had brought Henry the news, and The Horse's younger brother, The Hailstorm.

On the second day out, we camped on the bank of Laramie Creek under a huge, weather-beaten old cottonwood tree. We decided to stay here and wait for The Whirlwind. His

Setting Out for The Whirlwind's Village

location and movements were uncertain, but he would surely have to pass by us on his way to La Bonté's Camp. Besides, our horses were almost worn out from the rough ground, and I, myself, was in no condition to continue traveling. Henry sent The Horse on ahead to scout for The Whirlwind's people and to deliver a message to his squaw. She and her relatives were to leave the rest and push on as rapidly as possible to our camp.

After several days of rest, good water, and an abundance of game to eat, my strength began to return. But I was growing increasingly disturbed by the Indians' delay and cursed their untrustworthiness. At last, I announced, "Tomorrow morning I'll start for the fort to see if there's any news about the other war parties."

That night, The Horse returned from The Whirlwind's village. The chief was fifty miles south of us, moving slowly, and would not

Resting To Regain Lost Strength

arrive for at least a week. Henry's squaw was coming as fast as she could with her brothers, but she was dying and asking every moment for Henry.

Henry's manly face became clouded and downcast. "M'sieu Parkman, if you are willing, I will go in the morning to find her."

Quincy offered to ride with him, while I headed to the fort for news. So at sunrise, the three of us left camp.

At the fort, I was told that two large villages of Miniconjou Sioux had come 300 miles from the Missouri River to join in the war. They were gathering at Richard's Fort, not too far from Fort Laramie. I decided to ride over there, and what I found amazed me. It seems that the Sioux had met up with a company of emigrants heading for California. These emigrants had discovered that they were too loaded down with supplies, especially with Missouri whiskey. So they decided to sell some

Parkman Heads For the Fort.

to people at the fort and drink the rest. Therefore, the sight that greeted me was one of squaws stretched on piles of buffalo robes ... shabby Mexicans, armed with bows and arrows ... Indians ... long-haired Canadian trappers ... and American backwoodsmen displaying the well-beloved pistol and bowie knife — *and all were drunk!*

The next morning, back at Fort Laramie, I was talking to a trader named McCluskey when I saw a strange Indian leaning against the side of the gate. He was a tall, strong man, with heavy features.

"Who is he?" I asked McCluskey.

"Why, that's The Whirlwind, the feller what's made all this stir about the war," said McCluskey. "That's always the way with the Sioux. They never stop cuttin' each other's throats. 'Stead of sittin' in their lodges and makin' buffalo robes to trade with us in the winter, they go out lookin' for fights. If this

Drunken People at Richard's Fort

war goes on, we'll have poor tradin' with them next season, I reckon.''

The traders had all agreed with McCluskey and set about trying to convince The Whirlwind that it was also in *his* best interests that there be no war. After all, in a war, the Sioux would lose many horses and would not have time to hunt buffalo to trade with the white men.

By now The Whirlwind had grown bored with all the preparations for war, like a child grows bored of his favorite toy. So he agreed to give up his war.

But to further my own studies, I still hoped to see the Indian war ceremonies. And since The Whirlwind had already declared war to his Sioux nation, they were still going ahead with their plans to go on the warpath. Six large villages were bound for La Bonté's Camp to make preparations.

The day after I returned to our camp on

McCluskey Talks to The Whirlwind.

Laramie Creek, Quincy and Henry rode in. Henry had seen his squaw, who had stayed alive only long enough to speak with him. But on their way to our camp she had died. Her brothers had stayed behind to take care of the burial ceremonies, while Quincy and Henry had returned to camp. Henry was grief-stricken, and it was some time before his spirits revived.

A few days later, four young Indians, Henry's squaw's brothers, rode into our camp. They joined us for dinner, and as we passed the pipe afterwards, I asked them where The Whirlwind's village was.

"There," said Mahto-Tatonka, the youngest brother, pointing to the south. "They will reach here in two days."

"Will they go to the war?"

"Yes."

So, happily for my purpose, the traders had not changed The Whirlwind's mind, after all.

Henry's Squaw Is Dying.

Now, nothing would stop me from going to La Bonté's Camp to join in the ceremonies.

On the third day, when The Whirlwind's village did not arrive, we rode out to look for it. In place of the 800 Indians we expected, we met one lone savage riding toward us on the prairie. He told us that the Indians had changed their plan and would not come for at least three more days. The Indians' fickleness bothered me, but I would have to wait.

Four days later, a wild procession hurried in haste and disorder down the hill and over the plain below — horses, mules, dogs, heavily burdened *travois,* mounted warriors, squaws walking amid the throng, and a host of children. Soon, as if by magic, 150 tall lodges sprang up along the stream. The lonely plain was transformed into a swarming camp. The Whirlwind had arrived at last!

But would he go to war?

At length, the answer came. After all their

The Whirlwind Arrives At Last!

preparations, The Whirlwind and his warriors had decided not to go to the rendezvous at La Bonté's Camp. Instead, they intended to pass through the grim, lofty Black Hills and spend a few weeks hunting buffalo on the other side until they had killed enough to furnish them with a stock of provisions — the necessities of life: food, fuel, clothing, hides for their lodges, strings for their bows, coverings for their saddles, glue, thread, ropes, and vessels to hold water. The buffalo supplied all these needs and also provided the means of purchasing whatever else they wanted from the traders. So the buffalo hunt was essential for the Indians to survive. Then, after the hunt, they would send out their own small war party against the enemy.

What should I do? Stay with The Whirlwind or go on to La Bonté's Camp? It was possible that the other villages would be as changeable as The Whirlwind's. It was possible that no

Parkman Must Make a Decision.

Indians would be there. The trader Reynal was certain that none would be at La Bonté's Camp, so he was joining The Whirlwind in the Black Hills. Since we were still uncertain whether the villages would rendezvous or not, we decided to follow The Whirlwind too. After all, I remembered the old proverb about a bird in the hand being worth two in the bush!

We broke camp on the morning of July 1. We were not many miles from Fort Laramie when a trapper caught up with us. He was carrying a message from some trader friends of Henry's. They were going to La Bonté's Camp and wanted us to meet them. They assured us that ten or twelve villages would certainly assemble there. Quincy and I had a meeting and decided to go.

After several days of hard, tiring travel, we reached a plain. A line of tall, thick, misshapen trees blocked our view beyond the plain, but I knew what lay there.

A Trapper Brings a Message.

"Beyond those trees, Quincy, is the rendezvous place," I said. But my voice was the only sound to be heard in that long-looked-for place of rendezvous. We looked and listened anxiously. Forcing our horses through the trees, we saw the prairie beyond — not a plain covered with lodges and swarming with thousands of Indians, but "Nothing, Quincy, nothing . . . but desert!"

Quincy lashed his horse and galloped forward, letting out his anger with his swift ride. Although I was much more annoyed and disappointed than he, my illness had left me too weak to express my anger this way. So I followed at a quiet pace as the intolerably hot sun beat down on us. Not only weren't the Indians there, but the traders who were to meet us hadn't arrived either!

"Nothing . . . but Desert!"

"The Traders Are Not Coming."

CHAPTER 9

Indian Days

We decided to make camp and wait for news of the traders. I had come so far for my studies, I didn't want to miss the opportunity of rendezvousing with The Whirlwind. However, Quincy was losing patience.

"Look, Francis, we've been camped here two days waiting for those traders," he said. "Henry and I have scouted ten miles around in every direction, and we've seen no Indians, no buffalo — nothing but prairie. Like the Indians, the traders are not coming."

"Tell you what, Quincy," I suggested, "let's wait one more day, and if they don't come —

well then, Deslauriers can take the cart and baggage back to Fort Laramie while we try to overtake The Whirlwind's village."

"Francis, I'm afraid I'm not as interested in studying Indians as you. I'm exhausted, and my horse is disabled from climbing up and down all those ravines."

"In that case, I'll take Raymond and try to find The Whirlwind alone."

And so it was that after the last civilized meal we were to enjoy for some time, Raymond and I shook hands with our friends, agreeing to meet back at Fort Laramie on the first of August, and set off for the mountains.

As we crossed the gloomy Black Hills, we searched anxiously for hours for traces of the Indians. Failing to find them, we feared we had missed the trail. Then we saw the imprint of a moccasin, then the furrows made by dragged lodgepoles, then the tracks of many people and horses, then the ashes of 150 fires.

Parkman Leaves His Friends.

Excited, we went on, only to lose the trail on the hard ground and have to hunt for it again.

We slowly forced our animals over rocks, along narrow ravines, and through deep canyons where daylight could scarcely make its way. We edged past bare cliffs hundreds of feet high, with bald black crags as sharp as needles at the top.

All the while, I either hung in my saddle, hardly able to hold myself erect, or crawled up a steep rise on my hands and knees when my weary horse could no longer bear my weight.

After we entered the country roamed by the dangerous Shoshones and Arapahoes, we risked meeting any of their wandering parties — it would surely cost us our lives. Nothing remained of our supplies but a little flour. My strength, spirit, and horse were all about to give out.

It was then, a mile or more off, that we saw the tall lodges of the Oglala — one of the

Finding the Imprint of a Moccasin

bands of the western Sioux — standing in a circle by a stream. Horses and Indians swarmed everywhere. Never did the heart of a wanderer gladden more at the sight of home than did mine at the sight of that camp!

The trader Reynal was already with them, so they knew who I was and they welcomed me eagerly. For the next few weeks, that Oglala village was my home, and the chiefs and warriors, their squaws and children, became my family.

Raymond and I went to live in the lodge of Big Crow, who was honored that a white man should choose him as host. Our place was the guest's place, at the head of his lodge. We slept there on his buffalo robes and shared his pipes of tobacco and bowls of boiled buffalo meat.

Often, little naked, copper-colored boys and snake-eyed young squaws thrust their heads in through the tepee opening, inviting us to

Big Crow Welcomes Parkman.

various feasts in different parts of the village. Unless we wished to offend our hosts, we would have to pass from lodge to lodge, tasting in each one from the bowl of meat set before us and inhaling a whiff or two from our host's pipe. Since I was still suffering the effects of my illness, I was poorly qualified to eat twenty meals a day!

I knew, however, that at least half of our kind hosts, had they met us alone and unarmed on the prairie, would have robbed us of our horses and loosed an arrow on us besides.

I, of course, feasted the Indians in return. For some vermilion, beads, and other trinkets, I bought a white dog — the dish decreed by Sioux custom for all important occasions. For a few more trinkets, I hired two squaws to prepare the feast — the boiled dog. Raymond helped by frying what little flour we had left in buffalo fat and also made some well-sweetened tea. The feast was a resounding success and

Eating Twenty Meals a Day!

was followed by pipe-smoking and speech-making.

Reynal translated each sentence of my speech as I went along, and each was echoed by all my listeners with the usual cries of agreement and approval.

"I have come from a country so far off," I began, "that at the rate you travel, you could not reach it in a year."

"How! How!"

"There," I went on, "the whites are more numerous than the blades of grass on the prairie, and all their men are brave warriors."

"How! How! How!"

"While I was living in the white men's lodges, I heard of the Oglala — how great and brave a nation they are, how they love the whites, how well they can hunt the buffalo and strike their enemies. I resolved to come and see if all I heard is true...."

"How! How! How! How!"

Reynal Translates Parkman's Speech.

"I have not been able to bring many presents through the mountains. But at Fort Laramie I have plenty of powder, lead, knives, and tobacco — much better than the tobacco you get from the traders. And if you come to the fort before I go away, I will make you handsome presents."

"How! How! How! How!"

Then old Chief Red Water made his long reply, which Reynal translated for me. "I have always loved the whites. They are the wisest people on earth. They can do anything, and I am always glad when any of them come to live in our lodges. It is clear to me that you like the Oglala, or you never would have come so far to find our village." He chanted a song of thanks for the feast and then said, "Now let us go and give the white men a chance to breathe." And it was over.

The Oglala, I learned, were badly in need of skins to make their lodges for next year, for

Old Chief Red Water Replies.

their old ones were rotten and worn-out. Although they had enough buffalo bull skins, these were too thick and heavy to make lodges of. They needed buffalo cows, and the only place where these cows were plentiful was farther westward, near Medicine Bow Mountain at the entrance to the Rockies. Even though those hunting grounds belonged to the enemy Snake tribe, the Oglala felt their own warriors were brave enough. Besides, they had three white men with rifles (Reynal, Raymond, and myself) to help them.

So we broke camp and headed west. After traveling several days, we reached the hunting ground. Scouts advised us that buffalo had been spotted, and the general hunt was to take place the following day.

I galloped with my Oglala friends in the chase. While 70 of us charged headlong into a herd of 500 buffalo cows on one side, 30 more attacked the bewildered and panic-stricken

The Oglala Break Camp.

buffalo bulls on the other. Amid the trampling and yells, I could see their dark figures running hither and yon through clouds of dust as the horsemen darted after them.

The uproar and confusion lasted but a moment, and when the dust cleared, I could see the Indians riding behind the buffalo at furious speed, yelling as they shot arrow after arrow into their sides. Buffalo carcasses were scattered thickly over the ground. Here and there stood wounded cows, their bleeding sides feathered with arrows. As I rode by them, their eyes would glare. They would bristle like gigantic cats and feebly try to rush up and gore my horse.

At the end of five days of hunting, the Indians had brought in immense quantities of meat and hides. The meat was cut into thin sheets and hung on long cords between the lodges to dry in the sun. Squaws, young and old, labored on the fresh hides stretched on the

Chasing the Buffalo

ground. They scraped the hair from one side and flesh from the other, then rubbed buffalo brains into the hide to make it soft and easily bent. The skins were ready. Only the long poles to support them were needed. These poles were made only from the tall spruce trees of the Black Hills.

On July 25, the camp broke up with the usual hubbub and confusion, and we all moved once more, on horseback and afoot, over the plains. We traveled eastward back to the Black Hills.

After a two-day ride, we reached the tall spruces, which the Indians cut, peeled, and set out to dry and harden for several days in the sun. As we watched them, I saw Reynal gazing intently at the piles of black rocks that gave the hills their name.

"There's plenty of gold here," he said. "But the Indians say these hills are full of bad spirits, so it's dangerous for white men to go

Preparing the Buffalo Hides

gold hunting."

After the monotony of watching the tree-cutting for several days, I was glad when we were on the move again, back through the Black Hills, east toward Fort Laramie. I had promised to meet Quincy there on August 1, but on that day we were still trying to make our way through that wilderness of steep, rocky mountains and dark pine forests, with the fort still a two-day journey away. I was afraid that Quincy would worry, so, after a parting feast with our Oglala friends, Raymond and I pushed forward on our own.

Less than two days later, we rode through the swift current of Laramie Creek and up to the gateway of the fort, which seemed to me then the very center of civilization.

In a short time, I was seated with Quincy and Henry at breakfast. How pleased I was to be reunited with my gallant friends again!

Parkman and Raymond Return to Ft. Laramie.

Pike's Peak Rises over the Trail.

CHAPTER 10

On the Homeward Trail

On August 4, we began our long homeward journey from Fort Laramie. Our route along the Rockies to the Arkansas River took us through a country of burning plains whose only vegetation was a few tufts of short grass, dried and shriveled by the heat. We rode among hills crowned with a dreary growth of pines, and over prairies out of which rose snowy Pike's Peak.

Huge crickets, black and dark green, signaled our passing, and enormous wingless grasshoppers tumbled at our horses' feet.

Countless lizards darted like lightning among the tufts of grass, and large black squirrels leaped among the pine branches. Rattlesnakes as thick around as a strong man's arm slithered toward us, and we killed four or five a day.

We were not as concerned with the animal life we met as we were with other humans we might meet.

When we reached Bent's Fort on the Arkansas River three weeks and 425 miles later, we heard that the trail ahead to the settlements — some 600 miles — was in a dangerous state. Great numbers of hostile Pawnees and Comanches had gathered around some parts of it. But we trusted that kindly Good Fortune would continue to smile on us as she had thus far. Raymond left us at the fort, and we decided that the three of us would brave the danger as best we could.

Before we set out from the fort, however,

A Thick Rattlesnake Slithers Toward Them.

four men asked to join our group. Two were members of a party that had just brought in a large band of horses from California; the third was a Missourian who had gone halfway to Oregon and then became homesick; and the fourth was a soldier who had marched off to fight in the war with Mexico, but who had come down with brain fever on the way to Bent's Fort. He had been left at the fort with the rest of the sick, but was now recovered. We called all four "the California men" and welcomed them as reinforcements.

On August 27, we started off from the fort for the settlements. Certainly a more ragged cavalcade never was seen on the banks of the Upper Arkansas. In place of the large, fine horses with which we had left the frontier in the spring, we now rode the rough breed of prairie horses — as hardy as mules and almost as ugly. Despite our mules' strength and hardiness, they were already worn down by

Welcoming "the California Men"

hard service and were fast becoming footsore. Our saddles and equipment were worn and battered, and our weapons had become dull and rusty.

Our dress was shabby, and none looked shabbier than Quincy and I. He wore an old flannel shirt, flying open in front and belted around, while I, lacking anything else, was clothed in a time-worn buckskin suit. But we were as happy and careless as beggars as we crept slowly along the monotonous banks of the Arkansas.

A few days later, a long train of Santa Fe wagons came toward us, and a trader with them brought us news. "Well, boys, the bad news up ahead is Injuns. They been prowlin' 'round our camps every night. They raided a large party that left Bent's Fort couple-a weeks before you and killed a Massachusetts feller. His friends had buried him but when we found his grave, we discovered that the

The Indians Raided a Party from Bent's Fort.

Injuns'd dug him up and scalped him, and the wolves took care of the rest. Oh, I almos' forgot. The good news — there's lotsa buffalo up ahead."

The next day we met a long train of ox-drawn wagons loaded with government supplies for the troops. Their drivers told us that a large village of Arapahoes was camped farther along the river. They were supposed to be friendly, but there is a difference between a party of thirty men traveling with oxen, which Indians do not value, and our mere handful of men with a tempting band of horses and mules.

Late the following afternoon, we saw the Arapaho camp. Two hundred lodges stood in a grassy meadow beyond the river, while for a mile around on both banks of the Arkansas were scattered some 1500 horses and mules.

Meeting Arapahoes here on the Arkansas was a very different thing from meeting them

Coming Upon the Arapaho Camp

in their native mountains. But it was our good fortune to learn that when the army had passed them a few weeks before, the general had warned them that if they touched one hair of a white man's head, he would wipe out their entire nation. This placed them, for the time being, in an excellent frame of mind, and the effect of the general's threat had not yet disappeared.

And so, while the others moved on to get as far as possible from our suspicious neighbors before night fell, Quincy, Henry, and I rode across the river to visit the Arapaho village.

To the first Indian we met, Henry explained in sign language that we wanted to see the village and its people. The Indian looked at us with his little snake-like eyes, gathered his buffalo robe about his shoulders, and silently led the way toward the village.

The lodges resembled those of the Sioux in everything but cleanliness. Here, the ground

Visiting the Arapaho Village

was strewn with piles of waste buffalo meat. Hundreds of Indians flocked out of their lodges to look at us as we rode towards the chief's lodge. Here, we dismounted and sat down before the entrance, holding our horses' ropes in our hands and our rifles across our laps. We were soon shut in by a dense wall of savage faces whose features and complexions — unlike those of the Sioux — were exceedingly bad.

The chief, a mean-looking fellow, very tall, thin-faced, and muscular like the rest of his nation, came out and shook our hands. He called to a squaw within the lodge, who soon brought out a wooden bowl of meat, but, surprisingly, no pipe.

After tasting the meat as a matter of form, I began to open a bundle of presents. I wished to get one of their shields and offered a large piece of scarlet cloth, some tobacco, and a knife to anybody who would bring me one. The

The Chief Welcomes the White Men.

Arapahoes value their shields greatly and pass them on from father to son. A passable shield was brought to me. They wanted to know what we meant to do with it, and Henry made some signs in answer. When the effect was an instant chorus of shouts, obviously in our favor, I asked Henry what he had told them.

"Why," he replied, "I say we are going to use it to fight their enemies, the Pawnees."

The effect increased when we gave out more presents. Every face in the greedy crowd grinned, every eye glittered, and long, thin arms eagerly stretched toward us on all sides to receive the gifts.

That night after we returned to our camp, we were serenaded by the ferocious howls of hundreds of wolves, drawn by the garbage of the Arapaho village. Thinking of the more dangerous human wolves nearby, each of us spread our buffalo robe on the ground and kept our rifles tightly clasped in our arms.

Trading for an Arapaho Shield

The Plain Is Alive with Buffalo.

CHAPTER 11

Hunting the Wild Buffalo

As we continued eastward, the plain before us was alive with thousands of buffalo — bulls, cows, and calves. Far off beyond the river, they darkened the swelling prairie to the horizon. In many parts, they were crowded so thickly together that in the distance their rounded backs presented a surface of unbroken black. Elsewhere, the buffalo were more scattered, and here and there rose little columns of dust where some of them were rolling on the ground. We could see them rushing against each other and hear the clattering of their horns and their hoarse bellowing. With such a sight before us, only one thought could be on our minds, so Quincy and I rode down on them.

Over the next few days, we brought back many a buffalo tail to the party as a token of victory in the chase, and we roasted many a tasty tongue and juicy hump-rib over our fire.

We did so well on the hunt that we decided to camp in one place long enough to dry all the meat we would need for our jouney to the frontier — a journey we estimated might take a month. We pitched our tent by the side of the river — if the broad sand beds with a scanty stream of water flowing here and there along their surface deserve to be honored with the name of "river."

It was Deslauriers' task to cut the fresh meat into thin broad sheets for drying — an art in which he had all the skill of an Indian squaw. Soon cords of rawhide were stretched around the camp, and the meat was hung upon

Deslauriers Dries the Buffalo Meat.

them to dry in the sunshine and pure air of the prairie.

We kept Deslauriers well supplied with buffalo meat, since our frequent practice in the two methods used in hunting buffalo had added to our skill.

The first method was the chase on horseback, which goes by the name of "running." This is the more violent and dashing of the two, especially when the buffalo are in one of their wild moods. Otherwise, it is a tame enough method. An experienced and skillful hunter, well mounted, will sometimes kill five or six cows in a single chase, as he loads his gun again and again and rushes through the scrambling herd. With a bold and well-trained horse, the hunter may ride so close to the beasts that as they gallop side by side, he may touch them. This is not dangerous — so long as the buffalo remains strong.

But when the buffalo tires and can no longer

"Running" the Buffalo

run with ease and when his tongue hangs out and the foam flies from his jaws, then the hunter had better keep a respectful distance. For the troubled brute may turn upon him at any instant. The horse then leaps aside, and the hunter has need of a good grip on his saddle, for if he is thrown to the ground — farewell, hunter!

The chief difficulty in "running" buffalo is that of loading the gun or pistol at full gallop. To make the job easier, many hunters carry three or four bullets in their mouth. The bows and arrows which the Indians use in "running" buffalo have many advantages over firearms, and many white men do use them.

The second method of buffalo hunting, "approaching," is practiced on foot. The hunter using this method does not risk his horse breaking a leg in one of the prairie dog burrows and thus does not endanger his own life. But the hunter must be cool, collected,

Loading the Gun at a Gallop

and watchful. He must understand the buffalo, observe the features of the country and the course of the wind, and be well skilled in using his rifle.

Buffalo are strange animals. Sometimes they are so stupid that a man may walk up to them in full sight on the open prairie and even shoot several of them before the rest will think it necessary to retreat. At another moment, they will be so shy and wary that in order to approach them, the utmost skill, experience, and judgment are required.

Kit Carson, the famous hunter and guide, is, I believe, unmatched in "running" buffalo. In "approaching," Henry Chatillon is the champion. Henry had studied the buffalo as a scholar studies his books — and with as much pleasure. The buffalo were, in a sense, companions to him and, as he said, he never felt alone when they were about him.

Twice a day, at sunrise and noon, the buffalo

Henry, the Champion in "Approaching"

came from the hills to drink at the river near our camp. We would crouch under the river bank about twenty yards from the point where the well-worn buffalo path entered the water. We would hear the heavy, monotonous tread of the approaching bull. An enormous black head would be thrust out, the horns just visible amid the mass of tangled mane. He would clumsily make his way across the sand, his great shaggy back slowly swaying to and fro, and bend his head to drink.

As the water gurgled down his huge throat, we would noiselessly cock our rifle and sight him along our barrels. We would aim at a small bare spot just behind the point of his shoulder — this was our target. Lightly and delicately, our fingers would press the trigger.

CRACK! Instantly, in the middle of the bare spot, a small red dot would appear. The buffalo would shiver. He would not fall, but rather walk heavily forward, as if nothing had

Waiting for the Buffalo at the River Bank

happened. Yet before he went far out upon the sand, he would stop and totter. His knees would bend under him, and his head would sink forward to the ground. Then his whole vast body would sway to one side and roll over on the sand. And he would die without a noticeable struggle.

Ambushing the buffalo in this way when they came to drink was the easiest way to hunt them. We could also approach them by crawling up ravines, or behind hills, or even over the open prairie — often an easy task.

But at other times, it required the utmost skill of the most experienced hunter. Henry Chatillon was a man of remarkable strength and daring. But I have seen him return to camp quite worn-out from his efforts, his arms and legs scratched and wounded and his buckskin garments stuck full of the thorns among which he had been crawling.

On our second day at this camp, Henry went

The Buffalo Dies Without a Struggle.

out for an afternoon hunt. Quincy and I remained behind, but when we saw some bulls approaching the water on the other side of the river, we got our rifles, bullet pouches, and powder horns. Then we set off to attack them.

Nowhere was the water more than two feet deep, and we were almost across when the bulls saw us and began to move off swiftly. I climbed up the bank and ran after them. I was almost within gunshot distance when they slowly wheeled around towards me. Before they had turned far enough to see me, I fell flat on my face. The bulls stood and stared at the strange object in the grass. Then they turned away and walked on as before.

I rose and ran once more in pursuit. Again they wheeled around, and again I fell flat. After repeating this three or four times, I managed to get a shot off, from one hundred yards, at the largest buffalo I had ever seen. And I killed him!

Staring at the Strange Object in the Grass

Meanwhile, what had been an almost empty prairie when I began the chase was now thronged with a great multitude of buffalo. A heavy, dark column stretched to the right and left as far as I could see. Soon I began to hear at a distance on the left the sharp blasts of a rifle . . . again . . . again . . . and again.

Moving low and then crawling along the ground, I followed the sound. I had not gone far when, to my astonishment, I saw Henry standing erect upon the prairie, almost surrounded by the buffalo. He was at home.

Quite unaware that anyone was looking at him, Henry stood at the full height of his tall figure, one hand resting on his side and the other arm leaning carelessly on the muzzle of his rifle. His eye ranged over the buffalo. Now and then he would select a cow that suited him, level his rifle, and shoot her dead.

The buffalo paid as little attention to him as if he were just another buffalo. Some bulls

Henry Is at Home Surrounded by Buffalo.

bellowed and butted at each other; some rolled about in the dust. A group of buffalo would gather about the carcass of a dead cow, sniffing at her wounds. Now and then some old bull would face towards Henry with an air of stupid amazement, but none seemed inclined to attack or run away from him.

For some time I lay there, looking in surprise at this extraordinary sight. Finally, I crawled cautiously forward and, in a low voice, spoke Henry's name.

He turned, saw me, and said quietly, "Get up and come on."

I did as he said, and still the buffalo showed no sign of fear. They remained gathered about their dead companions. Henry had already killed as many cows as he wanted for our use, and I, kneeling behind one of the carcasses, shot five bulls before the rest thought it necessary to scatter.

After four days of work, we were ready to

Parkman Kneels Behind a Carcass and Shoots.

leave. We had 800 pounds of dried meat — the fattest and choicest parts of eight or nine cows. Only a small quantity had been taken from each cow, and the rest was left to the wolves.

By this time, the number of buffalo carcasses that lay about the nearby prairie, decaying under the hot sun, attracted wolves from every direction. There were large, red-eyed gray and white wolves and small prairie wolves not much bigger than a spaniel. The wolves would howl and fight in a crowd around a single carcass. And above them, the air was always full of turkey buzzards or black vultures, waiting to swoop down on the wolves' leavings.

As we resumed our journey eastward, multitudes of wolves were roaming over the neighboring prairie, and vultures in great clouds were soaring overhead. They would feast undisturbed.

Fighting Over the Buffalo Carcass

Meeting Volunteer Soldiers

CHAPTER 12

Along the Arkansas River

As we proceeded along the Arkansas River, we began to meet companies of Missouri soldiers. They were volunteers, following General Kearny's army on its march against Santa Fe in the Mexican territory. The soldiers were rough, but extremely good-looking men. They wore their knee boots, belts, and military trappings over ordinary civilian clothes and were armed with swords, holster pistols, and the excellent breech-loading Springfield rifles.

"How are you?" one fellow would greet us.

"Whar are you going?" asked another.

"Whar do you live when you're to home?" said a third.

"I reckon you're traders?" guessed a fourth.

"More buffalo up ahead?" another inquired.

"Reckon our horses can make it to Santa Fe?" still another asked.

Since each group of newcomers repeated the same questions, the bother soon grew unbearable. Our replies became shorter and crisper, and finally the soldiers went straggling away as they had come. Then, to our great relief, we were left alone again.

The buffalo were abundant, and we had as much hunting as we desired, both on horseback and on foot. But we did so with great care, for we were now in Pawnee country, and it would not do to be caught with an empty bullet pouch or powder horn.

Indeed, we now took every possible precaution. We mounted guard at night, each

Questions and More Questions

man standing in his turn. No one ever slept without drawing his rifle close to his side or folding it with him in his blanket.

One morning, our watchfulness was sharpened by finding traces of a large Indian camp. Henry studied the scene and concluded, "Comanche. A week old."

We sighed with relief that they were not any closer. But the next evening we found the ashes of a recent fire. That gave us some uneasiness.

Our uneasiness increased still further when we reached "The Caches," a place well known for its danger. It had a most threatening appearance. Sandhills were everywhere, broken by ravines and deep gullies. We found the grave of the Massachusetts man killed here some weeks before, probably by Pawnees, as the trader had told us. We did not delay.

"Keep a sharp lookout!" called Henry, and we spurred our horses, hurrying on as best we

A Recent Comanche Fire

could.

On the fourteenth of September, we saw a very large caravan of supplies bound for Santa Fe. The plain was covered with the long lines of white-topped wagons, black carriages in which the traders travel and sleep, large herds of horses and mules, and men on horseback and on foot. When they stopped near us, our party, with its tiny cart and handful of men, made a rather unimpressive appearance by the side of their wide and bustling camp.

One of the traders warned us, "Better not follow the main trail along the river, 'less you want to have your throats cut."

So here, where the river made a bend, we took a smaller trail that led directly across the prairie for sixty or seventy miles.

The following night, while I was suffering from the pain and weakness of the same illness that had attacked me in the mountains, a rainstorm came up. The moisture, which filled

A Caravan of Supplies Bound For Santa Fe

the tent and trickled from everything in it, did not add to my comfort.

About two hours after midnight, Quincy, who had been standing guard with one of the California men amid the rain and pitch-black darkness, came silently in. Touching Henry, he called to him in a low, quick voice, "Henry, I think you ought to come out."

"What is it?" I asked, jumping up.

"Indians, I believe," whispered Quincy. "But lie still. I'll call you if there's a fight."

He and Henry went out together. I took the cover off my rifle, prepared it for action, and then, being in much pain, lay down again. In about five minutes, Quincy returned.

"It's all right," he said, as he lay down to sleep. Henry was now standing guard in his place.

In the morning, Quincy told me the details of the alarm. "One of the California men thought he spotted some dark shapes down in

Quincy Wakens Henry.

the hollow among the horses, like men creeping on all fours. We got down flat on our faces and crawled to the edge of the bank overlooking the hollow. It didn't take long for us to be convinced those dark shapes *were* Indians. So I got Henry, and the three of us lay there watching. Well, you know Henry's eye is one of the best on the prairie. So it didn't take long for *him* to make out what those shapes were. Francis, they were nothing but *wolves!*"

"Strange," I wondered aloud, "that the horses didn't make a sound with those wolves creeping among them like that."

"Henry told me that all the wolves seemed to want was to gnaw on the rawhide trail ropes the horses were tied with," explained Quincy.

"Aha!" I cried with the pleasure of a detective solving a mystery. "So that explains why, several times on this journey, I've found my horse's trail rope bitten in two. Wolves!"

Wolves Gnawed On the Rawhide Trail Ropes.

The next day we came to a stream again, and from that time to the journey's end, we met long trains of government wagons almost every day. They were crawling at a snail's pace towards Santa Fe, laden with supplies for the troops.

At Cow Creek, we found the welcome novelty of ripe grapes and plums, which grew there in abundance. And at the Little Arkansas River, not much farther on, we saw our last buffalo, a miserable old bull, roaming over the prairie, sad and alone.

A Miserable Old Bull, Sad and Alone

Bagging Dozens of Prairie Hens

CHAPTER 13

To the Settlements . . . and Farewells

The country was changing every day. Behind us were the great arid deserts, thinly covered by tufts of shriveled pale green grass. Ahead of us were plains carpeted with rich greenery and sprinkled with flowers. In place of buffalo, we found plenty of prairie hens, which we bagged by the dozens without riding off the trail.

In three or four days, we saw ahead the forests and meadows of Council Grove. It seemed like a new experience, riding beneath the arches of noble trees like ash, oak, elm, hickory, and maple. All were hung with enormous grape vines, purple with fruit. The shouts of our scattered party rang through the breathless stillness of the forest. When we rode out again into the broad light of the open prairie, it was with regret.

Little more than a hundred miles now separated us from the frontier settlements. The country was one green prairie after another, rising in broad swells and relieved only by occasional clusters of trees following the course of a stream. These are the prairies of the poet and the novelist.

We had left danger behind us. Nothing was to be feared from the Indians of this region — the Sacs and Foxes, the Kansas and Osages. We had met with rare good fortune. For five months, our small party had traveled through a country where at any moment we could have been robbed of all we possessed, including our lives. But not a single animal had been stolen

Passing Through the Fruit-Laden Forests

from us — our only loss had been one old mule bitten to death by a rattlesnake. And not a single man in our party had been killed or wounded.

Three weeks after we reached the frontier, we learned that the Pawnees and Comanches had begun a regular series of raids along the Arkansas trail, killing men and driving off horses. They attacked every party, large or small, that passed that way during the next six months!

On a cheerless, rainy evening, we came to our last camping ground. But never was there a brighter fall morning than the one that followed, and we mounted once more, to return to the settlements.

We were passing through the country of the half-civilized Shawnees. It was a beautiful pageant of fertile plains and small woods just touched with the colors of autumn. Close beneath them nestled the log houses of the

Raids Along the Arkansas Trail

Indian farmers. Their shining yellow corn stood rustling in the wind, ripe and dry. Curved yellow squashes and huge orange pumpkins lay basking in the sun in the midst of their brown, shriveled leaves. Robins and blackbirds flew about the fences. Everything gave us proof that we were approaching civilization . . . home!

The forests that border the Missouri River soon rose before us. We had taken the same road on our outward journey in the spring, but now the road's appearance was totally changed. The wild young apple trees, fragrant with blossoms in the spring, were now thickly hung with their red fruit. Tall grass grew by the roadside in place of the tender shoots that months ago were just peeping from the warm and oozy soil. On every side we saw signs of full, ripe growth where, before, all had been fresh with opening life.

In the green light of the forest, squirrels

Approaching Civilization!

barked at us from the trees. Young partridges ran rustling over the fallen leaves, and the golden oriole, the bluejay, and the flaming redbird darted among the shadowy branches. We hailed these sights and sounds of beauty with mixed feelings.

As Quincy put it, "Civilization certainly has its charms. But you know, Francis, I'm kind of sorry to leave the wilderness."

At length, between the opening trees we saw the roof of a white man's house. Soon after, we were riding over the miserable log bridge that led into Westport. The town had surely seen strange scenes, but a rougher-looking troop than ours, with our worn equipment and broken-down horses, was never seen even there!

We passed many well-remembered buildings and camped in a meadow beyond. After taking leave of the California men and disposing of our horses and equipment, we hired a wagon

A Rough-Looking Troop Rides into Westport.

and drove to the Kansas landing. There, we found the log tavern that had housed us five months before, and from its porch we looked down once more on the little whirlpools of the Missouri River.

On the evening of the next day, Henry, Quincy, and I boarded a steamboat bound for St. Louis. Deslauriers, strangely transformed by a hat, a coat, and a razor, stood on a rock at the landing place, waiting to take leave of us.

"*Adieu! Mes amis, adieu, adieu!* Farewell! My friends, farewell, farewell!" he cried, as the boat pulled away. "When you go another time to de Rocky *Montagnes*, I will go with you! Yes, I will go!" He jumped about, swinging his hat, and as the boat rounded a distant point, the last thing we saw was Deslauriers still lifting his hat and skipping about the rock.

The passage down to St. Louis took eight days. During about a third of that time we were fast aground on sandbars. But once we

"Adieu! Mes Amis, Adieu, Adieu!"

reached our hotel, we found our trunks and, in the morning, transformed by the magic of the tailor's art, we hardly recognized each other.

The evening before we left for the East, Henry Chatillon came to say good-bye. No one who met him in the streets of St. Louis would have taken him in for a hunter fresh from the Rocky Mountains. He was very neatly and simply dressed in a suit of dark cloth. Although from the time he was fifteen he had rarely spent more than a month in a civilized town, he had a native good taste which always led him to pay great attention to his personal appearance. His tall, athletic figure and his fine face looked well with his present dress.

He had served us with a loyalty and devotion beyond all praise. We shook hands with regret, and he seemed to feel as we did. At Westport, Quincy had given him a horse, and I had given him my rifle. Perhaps at the very moment I write this, the rifle's sharp

Henry Comes To Say Good-bye.

voice is startling the echoes of the Rocky Mountains.

The next morning, we left St. Louis, and after two weeks of railroads, stagecoaches, and steamboats, we saw once more the familiar features of home.

It had been an exciting six-month, two-thousand-mile journey, during which we saw life that would cease to exist in the very near future, as the white man opened up and settled the West. Many of the Indians I had met and lived with would be destroyed; the mountain trappers and guides would be only a memory of the past; and the mighty buffalo would become all but extinct. But I consider myself fortunate to have been able to study these men and beasts at a time when the Wild West was still untamed and untouched by the white man.

Homeward Bound!

ILLUSTRATED CLASSIC EDITIONS

MOBY BOOKS

EC-EC/6-E4500-2/1544